i-SPY

in the park

SPY IT! SCORE IT!

Introduction

Parks are found everywhere you go. Whether you live in a city, or somewhere more rural, there's bound to be a park nearby.

They're full of great spots, from wildlife like squirrels and foxes, to colourful plants like lavender and daffodils.

There's also plenty to keep you active – if you find yourself in a park's playground, keep your eyes open for zip lines and helter skelters which can be a lot of fun. If the park has a lake or a pond, you might even be lucky enough to get a go on a pedalo or rowing boat!

Whatever park you find yourself in, there are sure to be some great spots, so keep your eyes peeled and getting spotting in the park!

How to use your i-SPY book

Keep your eyes peeled for the i-SPYs in the book.

If you spy it, score it by ticking the circle or star.

Items with a star are difficult to spot so you'll have to search high and low to find them.

50 POINTS

Once you score 1000 points, send away for your super i-SPY certificate. Follow the instructions on page 64 to find out how.

Playgrounds

Parks are great places to play. Many parks have exciting playground equipment for all ages.

Slide

Whizzing down a slide is always a thrill. There are slides of many shapes and sizes for different age groups.

10 POINTS

TOP SPOT!

Helter skelter

A helter skelter is a special slide which spirals down to the ground. Count the steps as you climb to the top and enjoy the twisting ride to the bottom.

40 POINTS

Swings

Swings are great fun and come in different shapes and sizes for all to enjoy. Some can hold more than one person.

5 POINTS

Playgrounds

Seesaw

A seesaw rocks up and down with riders balancing each other's weight. Most seesaws are for two people sitting down but some can have more riders in standing positions.

 5 POINTS

Roundabout

Roundabouts can hold various numbers of people, sometimes standing or sometimes seated. Do you enjoy going round and round? What about fast or slow?

 10 POINTS

Climbing frame

Standard, rigid climbing frames can be big or small. They challenge you to climb on, up, under, over and through them.

10 POINTS

Monkey bars

Swing from bar to bar like an ape through the treetops. Strong arms and good co-ordination are needed to get from one end to the other. **15** POINTS

Zip line

Zip lines usually have a handle to hang from or something to sit on like a tyre or seat. Unless they are supervised, they are close to the ground for safety.

 20 POINTS

Climbing wall or bouldering wall

Practise climbing skills by finding the best finger holds and placing your feet in the most stable positions.

 35 POINTS

Springer

Springers are one of the first playground rides that young children can use on their own. They are usually in the shape of animals or vehicles.

 10 POINTS

Spinner

A spinner is like a small roundabout. Sit in or on this equiment and spin until you feel dizzy!

 15 POINTS

Rope climber

These are special climbing frames using rope to provide an interesting and challenging climbing surface. Think of different ways of moving and climbing to the top.

 15 POINTS

Trees

Parks often contain a wide variety of tree species. You'll find many of the most popular British trees in parks, and other varieties might be found in an arboretum.

Oak

Oak trees can live for several hundred years, and are the most common tree native to Britain. Look out for their seeds (acorns) in the autumn.

10 POINTS

Trees

Sycamore

The sycamore is a tall tree with broad leaves. In the autumn its seeds spin to the ground in wing-shaped fruit.

10 POINTS

Horse chestnut

Growing into huge trees, horse chestnuts have a white and pink blossom in May and spiky green fruit in autumn that conceal the brown seeds of the tree.

10 POINTS

Beech

The beech tree is known as the queen of British trees and is home to a wide variety of wildlife.

15 POINTS

Holly

Holly has tough leaves with sharp spines to prevent animals from eating them. Its red berries are eaten by birds.

15 POINTS

Trees

Silver birch

The silver birch gets its name from the white peeling bark on its trunk. Its slender twigs droop, giving the tree a weeping effect.

15 POINTS

Pine

Pine trees are evergreen; they have green 'needles' and pine cones can often be found on the ground beneath the trees. Pine trees can vary in size.

10 POINTS

Wildlife

Parks, even those in the middle of large towns and cities, are teeming with wildlife. From larger mammals to tiny insects, there are plenty of creatures to see in the park.

Grey squirrel

Grey squirrels live in trees and are fantastic climbers. They are often seen scuttling across the ground or leaping between branches.

5 POINTS

TOP SPOT!

Red squirrel

The red squirrel is very rare. Like the grey squirrel, it lives in trees and eats acorns, nuts and tree seeds.

50 POINTS

5 POINTS

Duck

A variety of ducks live on the ponds and lakes within parks. It can be fun feeding the ducks in the park, but try to avoid bread – ducks prefer sweetcorn, peas and seeds.

Moorhen

Moorhens are black with a red and yellow beak. They are more timid than ducks and will swim into reeds at the edge of the pond if disturbed.

20 POINTS

Coot

Coots look similar to moorhens but are larger and have a white beak.

20 POINTS

Swan

Swans will live on larger duckponds, and on boating lakes in parks. Their white feathers and orange beak make them look very elegant.

15 POINTS

Pigeon

10 POINTS

There are a number of types of pigeons including the wood pigeon. Pigeons are common in the parks of large towns and cities.

Sparrow

5 POINTS

The sparrow is one of the most common birds in the park. They eat seeds and scraps and can often be quite tame around cafés and picnics.

Green woodpecker

The green woodpecker feeds mostly on the ground. Listen out for the rapid tapping sound as they peck holes in the dead wood of trees.

30 POINTS

Magpie

Magpies eat a wide range of food. They stand up to most other birds and are considered one of the most intelligent creatures.

10 POINTS

Blackbird

It is only the male blackbird that is black with a yellow beak. They eat insects, worms, fruit and berries.

10 POINTS

Song thrush

As the name suggests, the song thrush is quite vocal. You'll usually spot one in a tree or a bush, or sometimes on the ground finding snails to eat.

 15 POINTS

Robin

With its bright red breast, robins are easy to spot. They are quick to chase other birds away if they get too close.

 5 POINTS

Blue tit

With a mix of blue, yellow, white and green feathers, blue tits are very recognisable. They love insects, caterpillars, seeds and nuts.

 15 POINTS

Wildlife

Seagull

10 POINTS

Seagulls fly and live inland as well as by the sea. Large groups of them can often be seen in town and city parks looking for scraps of food.

TOP SPOT!

40 POINTS

Bat

Bats are flying mammals. They eat insects as they fly and are easier to spot as it starts to go dark in summer months, flying around trees and low over ponds.

Rat

Love them or loathe them, rats are never far away when humans are present. They are quick to find food waste and other litter.

35 POINTS

Mole

Moles are very difficult to spot as they live underground. Look out for molehills where the moles have popped up to the surface. Score 20 points for spotting a molehill and 40 points for seeing an actual mole!

20 POINTS

Score double for seeing an actual mole.

Deer

Although many deer species are quite large, they can be seen in some parks as they graze on grass, or eat leaves and berries. They are often timid and will run away if startled.

30 POINTS

Hedgehog

Despite being nocturnal, hedgehogs can sometimes be spotted during the day. Hedgehogs generally eat insects and slugs.

30 POINTS

Bee

Bees are such important creatures, pollinating plants and crops. Different types of bee such as bumblebees or honeybees can be seen, usually around flowers.

5 POINTS

Butterfly

There are many species of butterflies of many different colours that may be spotted flying between the different plants, trees and shrubs in the park.

Spider and web

Spiders are everywhere. Look out for a spider on its web, carefully spun to catch flying insects for food. On damp or frosty mornings the delicate webs sparkle in the light.

Snail

Snails eat most things, and can do damage to plants. They take cover in their shell if threatened.

Rabbit

Rabbits burrow into the ground to make their homes, and like a nice supply of vegetation nearby.

20 POINTS

Caterpillar

A caterpillar is the larva of a butterfly or moth. They feed on leaves and other vegetation.

15 POINTS

15 POINTS

Slug

Slugs are similar to snails but have no shell. They eat plant leaves, stems and roots so are unpopular with gardeners.

Common lizard

The common lizard can sometimes be found in parks. Look out for them basking in the hot sun during summer months.

40 POINTS

Grass snake

The longest snake in the UK is harmless. They eat small mammals and amphibians so can sometimes be spotted near or in ponds and lakes.

50 POINTS

TOP SPOT!

Fox

Foxes are members of the dog family. They are common in parks as there is plenty for them to eat.

30 POINTS

Frog

Frogs are amphibious (meaning they can live both on land and in water). They'll often be seen near or in ponds, and they eat insects, snails, slugs and worms.

20 POINTS

Dragonfly

Dragonflies are large flying insects. Look out for their vivid colours as they fly over ponds and lakes.

20 POINTS

Newt

Newts are amphibians, breeding in ponds during the spring. For the rest of the year they live in woods, grassland, hedges and marshes and eat insects.

40 POINTS

Water

*Many parks have at least one, and often many, water features.
These can be ornamental or put there for everyone to have fun.*

Duck pond

Ducks and other waterfowl live on the pond and
visitors can usually watch and feed the ducks.

5 POINTS

Water

Boating lake

Some parks will have larger ponds or even small lakes on which small boats or pedaloes can be hired for a relaxing hour or two on the water.

15 POINTS

Paddling pool

Children love a paddling pool for great water fun in warmer weather. Paddling, sitting or even swimming in the shallow water is so refreshing.

20 POINTS

Splash pad

A splash pad often has different jets of water squirting out of the ground or objects dotted around the area. They're great fun for splasing around!

20 POINTS

Fountain

Fountains of all shapes and sizes appear in parks, sometimes as part of a smaller stone feaure, sometimes as large fountains in the middle of ponds or lakes.

15 POINTS

Swimming pool

Some parks have an open-air swimming pool or lido. They are usually open in summer months but some hardy swimmers will take a dip in the middle of winter too.

40 POINTS

TOP SPOT!

Sports

Parks provide wide open spaces that allow great opportunities for sports. Even smaller parks often have dedicated areas for various sports to take place.

Tennis

Many parks have tennis courts. In some parks, tennis rackets and balls can be hired so anyone can play.

15 POINTS

Football

Larger parks might have room for full-size football pitches, but even smaller parks may have small pitches or football cages.

10 POINTS

Jogging

10 POINTS

Parks provide pleasant, traffic-free paths for jogging around. Joggers of all abilities and ages can be seen in the park.

Bowls

Bowls is played on a grass bowling green. Players take turns rolling (bowling) the bowl towards a smaller bowl called a jack, with the player closest being the winner.

15 POINTS

Boules

Like bowls, boules involves aiming for a smaller ball with the closest player being declared the winner. In boules the metal boule is tossed into the air. It is usuallly played on gravel or sand.

30 POINTS

Basketball

Basketball hoops and even full courts can be seen in many parks. They sometimes share tennis courts or smaller football pitches.

15 POINTS

40 POINTS

Disc golf

Spread over a wide area in larger parks, disc golf requires a frisbee disc to be aimed at baskets. The winner is usually the person to take the fewest shots around the course.

Skateboarding

Skate parks can be found in many parks. Look out for ramps, banks, pipes and rails for skateboarders to practise and showcase their skills.

20 POINTS

Skating

In-line or roller skating is great fun on any relatively smooth and firm surface. Look out for skaters on the many paths around the park.

20 POINTS

Table tennis

Some parks have outdoor table tennis tables. Bats and balls can usually be hired for a small fee.

30 POINTS

Orienteering

Look out for orienteering checkpoints that orienteers have to find using special maps of the park.

Pitch and putt

Golf requires huge golf courses but its baby sibling, pitch and putt needs much less space. Courses will usually have 9 or 18 holes and equipment can be hired.

BMX track

BMX tracks allow riders to race or just ride around practising skills on their BMX bike.

Food and drink

All of the vistors to the park need food and drink. Whether taking their own, or having opportunities to buy snacks, the park is a lovely place to stop and eat.

Ice cream

Whether it's from an ice cream van, a kiosk selling ice cream, or even a park café, spot somebody else or even yourself eating an ice cream.

10 POINTS

Barbecue

While barbecues are neither allowed nor advisable in some parts of a park, look out for special barbecue areas.

20 POINTS

Picnic

It could be your own or another family having a picnic. Share a blanket on the ground and share some tasty treats on a summer's day.

15 POINTS

Coffee shop or stall

A drink of coffee while sitting or walking around a peaceful park is sheer bliss for some people. Cafés or kiosks will often sell coffee.

15 POINTS

Food and drink

Café

If the park is large enough, there may be a café selling anything from small snacks to more substantial meals.

15 POINTS

Drinking fountain

Some parks have drinking fountains in various places to allow visitors a free drink of water as they take in the park's delights.

20 POINTS

Activities

There are so many things to do in the parks of the United Kingdom. While some people just enjoy a walk around the park, there are plenty of other activities to spot.

Rowing boat

Rowing boats can be hired on boating lakes in some parks. It's tricky to get the right rhythm but it can be great fun rowing around the lake.

40 POINTS

Pedalo

Pedaloes float on the water and move along by pedal power. Spot them on boating lakes or ponds in some parks.

40 POINTS

Activities

Nature trail

All of the wildlife in parks makes them ideal places for nature trails. There might be signs or information boards helping to direct people around the trail.

30 POINTS

Fitness trail

Fitness trails have different fitness activities and challenges connected by paths.

30 POINTS

Cycling

There will be some areas of the park where cycling is not allowed but there are usually plenty of paths to ride a bike safely away from traffic.

10 POINTS

Kite flying

Look out for kites flying in the air above large open spaces in parks on a windy day.

20 POINTS

40 POINTS

Funfair

Travelling fairs will sometimes visit parks, providing all the fun of the fair for a few days. Try out the different rides.

Crazy golf

Without the need for many golf skills, crazy golf can be great family fun. Steer the ball through the obstacles and into the hole.

30 POINTS

Activities

Horse riding

Some parks have special areas or bridleways for riding horses.

 30 POINTS

Photography

Whether it's selfies in the park or snapping the wildlife, there is always something to take a photograph of in the park.

20 POINTS

Drawing and painting

Patiently drawing and painting nature and other aspects of park life, artists love the variety of subjects in the park.

 30 POINTS

Exercise classes

Some parks, particularly in summer months, hold outdoor exercise classes such as aerobics or yoga.

20 POINTS

Outdoor gym

Outdoor gym equipment can be great fun and encourages people to keep fit and healthy.

30 POINTS

TOP SPOT!

40 POINTS

Chess

Chess boards are sometimes marked onto tables in the park ready for anyone to enjoy a game of chess.

Activities

Musical instruments

Chimes, pipes, drums and other instruments can specially be designed for outdoor play and fixed in the park for all to enjoy.

20 POINTS

Dog walking

Dogs on leads are welcome in most areas of the park, and there may be special areas for owners to let their dogs run free too.

10 POINTS

Plants and flowers

Parks usually have many different plants and flowers that not only look beautiful but also attract wildlife.

Ornamental garden

Ornamental gardens are carefully designed, often with geometric patterns of flower beds and paths.

10 POINTS

Sensory garden

Features, objects and plants stimulate the senses of touch, smell, hearing, sight and sometimes even taste.

15 POINTS

Rose

Roses flower in the summer in a variety of different colours. Most will be in flower beds but climbing roses can also be seen on trellises and walls.

10 POINTS

Plants and flowers

Daffodil

Daffodils are bright yellow flowers and are often abundant in the spring, growing in borders and grass.

 5 POINTS

Pansy

Pansies have colourful flowers and are often seen in flower beds around the park.

 5 POINTS

Lavender

Lavender is a bushy plant with strongly scented flowers. Birds love lavender seeds and bees love its blue flowers.

 15 POINTS

Tree blossom

Many trees have blossom that can be seen in the spring. The blossom adds colour to the park and will carpet the floor as it falls.

 10 POINTS

Ivy

Ivy is a climbing plant that attaches itself to walls and trees, often taking over if left unchecked.

 10 POINTS

Dandelion

Look out for bright yellow flowers or the feathery white seeds that float away on the wind.

 5 POINTS

Plants and flowers

Daisy

Daisies often grow in grass and can sometimes look like a white blanket of snow over a green lawn.

5 POINTS

Foxglove

With their spires of bell-shaped flowers, foxgloves are vibrant in colour and attract bees.

15 POINTS

Bluebells

Look out for bluebells late in the spring, especially in wooded areas where the blue, bell-shaped flowers add wonderful colour to the woodland floor.

10 POINTS

Park buildings and structures

There are many buildings and structures in our parks. Some provide services for visitors while others are simply nice to look at.

Museum

Some parks have a museum, often related to local history rather than just the park itself.

40 POINTS

Conservatory or tropical plant house

Made of glass, these often ornate structures provide ideal light and temperatures for plant varieties that would not usually grow in the UK.

30 POINTS

Park buildings and structures

Pagoda

A pagoda is a tower with ornate tiers. Originating in Asian countries such as China and Japan, pagodas are used as ornamental features in some parks.

40 POINTS

Clock

20 POINTS

A large clock may be on display in the park. It could be attached to a prominent wall or could have its own structure.

Toilets

5 POINTS

Toilets are needed for park visitors. Larger parks may have more than one building for toilets.

 Toilets

Bandstand

A bandstand is a special sturcture, often circular, with a roof. Traditionally, a band will use the bandstand to entertain park visitors.

15 POINTS

Bird hide

Bird hides are specially designed for watching birds without startling or disturbing them. They are usually coloured to blend in with the surroundings.

30 POINTS

Pavilion

Many parks have a pavilion. These buildings often contain seating, toilets and a café or restaurant.

15 POINTS

Statues and memorials

Parks are often home to memorials and statues. Both can be of varying size and importance.

War memorial

War memorials usually remember those who have died in war. They often contain the names of local soldiers who gave their lives.

30 POINTS

Famous person statue

Famous people are often commemorated with a statue. They are sometimes people from the local area.

30 POINTS

Animal statue or carving

Statues of animals are often favourites of children.

25 POINTS

Character statue

Some statues depict characters from films or books, particularly stories for children.

25 POINTS

Memorial plaque

Plaques remembering somebody are often placed next to trees or on park benches.

10 POINTS

Events

Organised events often make use of the space our parks provide. The local and wider community can join in, often for free.

Parkrun

Saturday mornings see large groups of runners taking part in their local parkrun in parks all over the country.

10 POINTS

Sponsored walk

Parks are great places for sponsored events. Look out for people walking (or maybe even running) laps of the park raising money for charity.

20 POINTS

Live music

With open spaces and plenty of grass to sit on, musicians might organise concerts, playing their music for audiences of diffent sizes.

15 POINTS

Displays

From motorbike stunts to dog agility, cheerleaders to mock battles, be on the lookout for organised displays to entertain the public.

15 POINTS

Seasons

The park is ever-changing with the seasons. Plants and animals look or behave differently, people do different things, and the weather changes througout the year.

Leafless trees

Many winter trees have no leaves. Look at the shapes made by their branches, which are more difffcult to spot in summer months.

Snow

Look out for the snow-covered ground in the winter. Be the first to make footprints in the pure white snow.

Ice

Ice will form on ponds and lakes, as well as creating magical icicles from trees and buildings during winter.

10 POINTS

Sledging

If the park has a hill, snowy days will often attract visitors with their sledges. Join in or watch them zoom down the slope.

15 POINTS

Early spring flowers

Look out for early spring flowers such as crocuses and snowdrops, indicating slightly warmer and longer days.

10 POINTS

Buds

Buds begin to appear on trees in the spring, eventually become the new leaves.

10 POINTS

Baby animals

Baby animals such as ducklings can be spotted during the spring, often watched over by their mother.

10 POINTS

Leaves

Trees in the summer are covered in rich, green foliage. All of these leaves capture the sunlight, helping the tree to grow.

5 POINTS

Sunbathing

Parks provide great spaces for people to relax. Look out for people lying in the warm sun during the summer months.

15 POINTS

Autumn leaves

The autumn leaves turn brown, gold and red. Look out for the wonderful colours of trees and for leaves fallen to the ground.

5 POINTS

Conkers

Look for the hard brown seeds of the horse chestnut tree. They fall from the tree in green spiky cases, which split open to reveal 'conkers'.

10 POINTS

Park signs

Signs are everywhere. They give information, warn of dangers, provide directions and tell us where we are.

Park name

Look out for the name of the park. It will usually be near at least one of the park entrances.

10 POINTS

Dunfermline Public Park

Map board

Maps are great for showing us where things are in the park. There will often be a mark on the map showing your current position.

30 POINTS

No motor vehicles

Parks are usually traffic-free spaces. Signs will warn drivers that they cannot enter the park.

15 POINTS

Cycle path

To ensure safety for all, some paths might be designated as cycle paths with signs painted on the ground.

10 POINTS

No cycling

Bicycles are sometimes not wanted in some parts of the park, so 'No cycling' signs let cyclists know this.

No cycling

10 POINTS

Directions

Signs showing the directions of different parts of the park help visitors to find their way.

5 POINTS

No ball games

While parks are great spaces for playing, some areas might be more peaceful or contain delicate plants and flowers. Ball games could break the peace and damage plants.

20 POINTS

Keep off the grass

Occasionally some special lawn areas are to be looked at rather than walked on.

20 POINTS

People watching

All sorts of people work at the park, or are vistors. The park can be enjoyed by everyone, no matter what age, and people working there help it to be a lovely, safe place for all.

Park keeper

The park keeper is in charge of the park. It is their job to check that all parts of the park are used as they should be and that everything is looked after.

20 POINTS

Gardener

Plants, trees and flowers need looking after and parks rely on a team of gardeners to keep them looking beautiful.

10 POINTS

People watching

Park police

In larger cities, parks can have police officers who patrol the park, ensuring people and property are safe.

Litter picker

Unfortunately, so many visitors to the park often means that there will also be litter left lying around. Park staff or volunteers will often collect this litter.

Famous parks

There are over 25,000 parks in the UK varying in size from small village playgrounds to large city parks. Some of these parks are very well known.

Hyde Park

Hyde Park is one of London's eight Royal Parks. It covers a very large area, has a big boating lake called the Serpentine, and the Diana Memorial Fountain.

15 POINTS

The Regent's Park

This is another of London's Royal Parks. Key features of the park include a wetland area for birds, an open air theatre and London Zoo.

15 POINTS

Famous parks

15 POINTS

Heaton Park

Heaton Park is a large park in the north of Manchester. There are playgrounds, a boating lake, sporting facilities and an animal centre among its many attractions.

Sefton Park

Sefton Park in Liverpool has many statues and monuments, a large playground and the famous glass Palm House with plants from around the world.

15 POINTS

Cannon Hill Park

Cannon Hill Park in Birmingham has swan-shaped pedaloes on its boating lake. A land train helps visitors get around the park and visit other attractions such as the nature centre.

15 POINTS

Roundhay Park

Roundhay Park in Leeds is one of the largest parks in Europe. It has a wide range of facilities, sports pitches and playgrounds.

15 POINTS

Roath Park

Roath Park in Cardiff is a late-Victorian park with a Botanic Garden, Wild Garden and the famous Scott Memorial Lighthouse.

15 POINTS

Victoria Park

Victoria Park in Belfast is home to various water birds on its beautiful lake, which has walking trails around it.

15 POINTS

Famous parks

Princes Street Gardens

In the heart of Edinburgh, Princes Street Gardens offers a peaceful place to enjoy the many flower beds, trees and everything else the park has to offer.

15 POINTS

Glasgow Green

In the centre of Glasgow, Glasgow Green is home to statues, a museum, trees, plants and wildlife. It also has the world's largest terracotta fountain.

15 POINTS

Index

i-SPY

How to get your i-SPY certificate and badge

Let us know when you've become a super-spotter with 1000 points and we'll send you a special certificate and badge!

Here's what to do:

- Ask an adult to check your score.

- Apply for your certificate at www.collins.co.uk/i-SPY (if you are under the age of 13 we'll need a parent or guardian to do this).

- We'll email your certificate and post you a brilliant badge!